You, the Magician

Written by

Josh Carothers & Jodi Maestas Carothers

Illustrated by

Kendra Shedenhelm

Yay!

For ALL
—JC

For Ivan & Paula, my favorite kids
—JMC

For Archer
—KS

Text copyright © 2014 by Josh Carothers & Jodi Maestas Carothers
Illustrations copyright © 2014 by Kendra Shedenhelm

ISBN 978-0-9909609-0-4

www.youthemagician.com

Since you are reading this book,
it is written for you.

The path has been cleared,
just follow your clues.

We're so happy you found us,
now we can go!

What makes you excited?
Do you want to know?

What if this is a dream?
Are you sure you're awake?

Follow your joy, for there are no mistakes.

If you'd like to go further,
then let us explain...

Built-in you,

it's waiting...

just quiet your brain.

5 senses can guide you:
Touch,
Taste,
See
and Smell,
Hear.

But you're born with a 6th
that can help make things clear.

Talk to your gut,
don't be afraid.

It wants you to trust it.
What does it say?

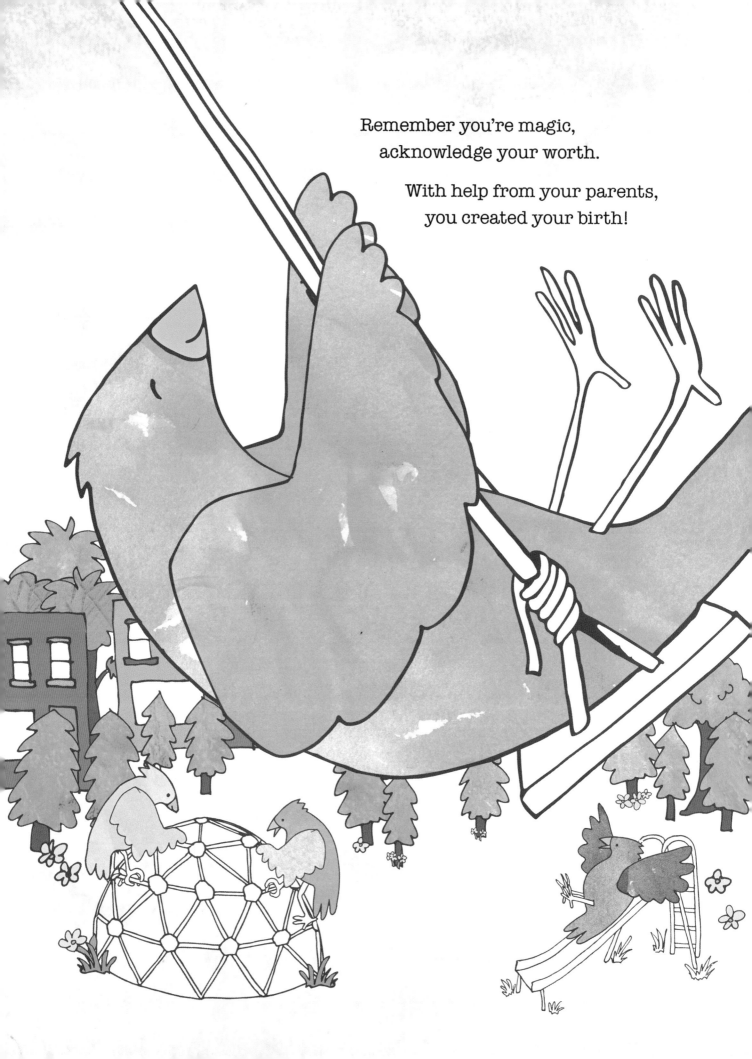

Remember you're magic,
acknowledge your worth.

With help from your parents,
you created your birth!

Observe your performance,
your daily routine.

You make yourself up
to teach yourself things.

Let's set the stage:
Look at life as a game.

You choose your adventure,
you star in your play.

Quest and be curious,
there's nothing to lose.

Try out new directions,
like trying on shoes!

If you're stuck in a maze,
just change your mind.

You'll realize it's YOU
who's in charge at all times.

As a daily reminder,
tell yourself this,

"I believe in myself.
I create what I wish."

Don't be so certain
with one of two angles.

Take a third point of view
to comb through the tangles.

There's a lot more to life
than what we've been told.

If you don't ask the questions,
how will you know?

No-thing is solid,
even science agrees.

There are molecules
dancing
at various speeds.

Photons
and bosons
and waves are unseen.

The thicker the substance,
the slower they beat.

A clock is a loop, not a straight line.

When you live
in
the
moment,
you are not locked in time.

Be open to notice
what's right in your face.

We've traveled through time
to get to this place.

There's more to the story
than the Human race.

For we live on a planet
floating in space!

Some people go left,

some people go right.

Dividing ourselves has taught us to fight.

There's no need to battle,
there's No-thing to prove.

When you see that ALL things
are reflections of you.

Let your heart drive, it reminds you to dream.
It offers the key to awaken from sleep.

YOU
are the language of Mystery and Magic.

There's no reason to worry,
for life is FANTASTIC!

You are the Magician,
creating and causing.

Conducting the story,
the sound of me talking.

Made in the USA
Charleston, SC
18 November 2014